F

DAVID ANSON RUSSO

THE ULTIMATE
Maze Book

Introduction by DEBORAH BERGMAN

A *FIRESIDE BOOK*   *Published by Simon & Schuster*
New York   London   Toronto   Sydney   Tokyo   Singapore

Frontispiece illustration
is the Inner Sanctum maze
and preface illustration
is the Tri-star maze,
both by David Anson Russo.

F

FIRESIDE
Simon & Schuster Building
Rockefeller Center
1230 Avenue of the Americas
New York, New York 10020

Designed by Laurie Jewell
Manufactured in Hong Kong

1   3   5   7   9   10   8   6   4   2

ISBN 0-671-73017-7

Editorial Consultant: Deborah Bergman

Contents

ACKNOWLEDGMENTS

To THE DOLPHINS

Preface

MY MAZES have everything to do with my spiritual life. Each time I am inspired by an archetypal symbol and find within it the beginning and ending of a maze, I know I'm about to explore another aspect of the journey of existence. And each time I plant an obstacle or devise an escape along the way, in my own mind I'm artistically depicting a new challenge in the odyssey each of us undertakes in our experiences on the soul level to achieve our ultimate goal: the integration of spiritual potential and life experience, the ending that is also a new beginning.

I make mazes because they are interactive art, because for me making a beautiful piece of work is not enough. What drives me artistically is to make the art and the viewer one. I want more than a momentary glance from you. I don't consider my mazes finished until you try to solve them. This way you actually become an integral part of each maze as you learn its ins and outs, corners and dead ends.

As a game, the defining characteristic of the maze is that it is very primal, unlike "acquired knowledge" puzzles like crosswords. To win at mazes you don't need to have an extensive grasp of vocabulary and facts. All you need are your instinctive decision-making skills and a little patience. Remember, no matter how difficult a maze of mine may seem, you can finish it. You're born with all the intellect you need to successfully navigate these mazes and accomplish your task.

To challenge you, I build in quite a bit of psychological warfare as I design each maze. Tricking or deceiving an opponent was one of the basic tenets of mazes when they were invented in ancient times, and one of my favorite ploys is to overload your mind by suddenly giving it a multitude of possibilities from which to choose. More specifically, imagine you are deep in a maze following a straightaway path with just a few offshoots. This path seems to be leading you closer and closer to your goal. You feel pretty comfortable following it; you don't have to make too many choices along the way, and there's not too much work for you to do but follow along.

Suddenly, I'll bring you to an intersection of about six to eight trails and your first big decision. I give you this excessive number of choices to overwhelm you and tempt you into making a random pick. Generally, the trails that look as though they take you right to your goal will actually lead you far from it: in my mazes, there is no "easy street." Maybe two of the six to eight paths will actually bring you closer to your goal, and probably only one of these will take you straight to the finish. This winning trail will appear to be leading in the direction opposite of the one where you want to go. Psychologically speaking, you will hardly choose a trail that seems to lead you back the way you came. It doesn't conform to your comfort pattern.

Another favorite deception of mine is to hide a trail entrance right under your nose. A third is to twist and turn a path in such a way that you pass up the winning trail and stay with a more seemingly direct artery. And the smaller a maze of mine is, the harder it is likely to be. There are more tricks, but they're trade secrets.

It will help you to remember that human beings as a species are a little impatient. By nature, we prefer immediate gratification with as little effort expended as possible. When I make a maze I take advantage of this trait any way I can. So if you know you're in one of my traps, stop to carefully analyze the problem confronting you. As the Zen master said, *be here now.* Then, analyze me. When you play my game, it only seems as if you're playing it alone. I am the other player, and you are playing my mind. I set up a scenario, a situation full of dead ends, swirling eddies, infinity signs, and other hypnotizing obstacles, and for a short time you journey through it. And unless you give up, you'll eventually beat me, because I won't be in front of you to counter your every move.

In every maze I make, whatever corner, nook, or cranny you find yourself in, a winning path will be at your disposal. I never include just a single successful trail, the way Daedalus did when he designed the first labyrinth.

I also make mazes in other mediums. I've created full-sized walk-through hedge mazes called living sculptures. They're generally simpler in design than two-dimensional mazes because when someone actually walks through a maze, the perspective changes. There is no visual overview to show escapes or where the goal lies; all you know is where you are and where you've been. I also make three-dimensional maze sculptures on large wood turned bowls. Carved in relief, with tunnels, bridges, and other wonderful features, they run around the bowls' centerpiece. I think these are the most aesthetically beautiful mazes, and they're workable, too.

Whatever form I'm working in, I want to bring you into my world, to make you an integral part of my work. It just isn't complete without you. And remember—if you get through these mazes, then you're better than I am. Because I don't solve mazes. I just create them!

NOTE The mazes can be worked on the page, but if you would prefer not writing on the actual book page another option would be to use a piece of tracing paper or acetate.

Introduction

PERHAPS no other pastime but playing cards, whose rich symbolism gave birth to the Tarot, can offer us as much potential for self-discovery and spiritual growth as the maze. Like Tarot, a maze presents us with a special opportunity to be both enlightened and entertained. As we move along a maze's paths and discover our own new and individual solutions to one of the world's most ancient type of puzzles, play and profound experience become one and we find that each new and stimulating challenge we face in this game carries echoes of our cultural and spiritual past.

This apparent blending of opposites is more than a good description of the pleasures of maze solving. It also characterizes the essence of the maze. In the West, the game reveals traditions from the ancient labyrinths, underground mazes erected to ritualistically create and guard the point in time and space where life connects with death and where secret knowledge and power originate as the result of this integration of these most essential polarities. The maze also bears a striking resemblance to the intricately patterned mandalas of the East. The classic mandala's circular shape and centerpoint symbolize the integration of all opposites in the universe into a single, encompassing whole. The mandala is used as an aid to meditation, which creates different types of integration in the awareness of the beholder. And one of the maze's properties is its ability to function as an "active" mandala, one that fulfills its purpose not by being receptively absorbed but rather by being "solved" by a player who meets the challenges its trails represent in order to ultimately touch the centerpoint that symbolizes power and integration.

This multicultural, ancient ability to fuse opposites and confer power sheds quite a bit of light on the reasons for the maze's enduring appeal and its attraction for artists like David Anson Russo. Whether we create or follow a maze's paths, the form allows us to experience the satisfaction of appreciating all its minute detail, paralleling the detail of the natural world, even as we also experience the deeper whole, or integration. As we add this pair to our list of opposites, let's consider the interconnected history of labyrinths and mazes by first addressing each form.

The terms "maze" and "labyrinth" are used interchangeably in common parlance and throughout written history. In fact, dictionaries often list each word as the other's definition. However, there is another school of thought, to which David Russo belongs, that makes a clear distinction between the two forms. This school of thought is best expressed by Edmund Carpenter, a noted anthropologist and authority on mazes and labyrinths. He believes that mazes and labyrinths are closely related in their ancestry, and that the primary difference lies in how they are drawn:

> A maze is a puzzle, a hazardous mantrap. False turnings and blind endings obstruct passage. That is the maze's purpose. One is supposed to get lost in it, never escaping and, therefore, suffering eternal frustration. By contrast, one cannot get lost in the classic labyrinth. Its unicursal path guarantees safe passage. In any true labyrinth, participants must cover the entire ground by one pathway, and one pathway only. Nothing should block that path, nor should any openings occur in its walls, as do occur in mazes. Continuity of passage is mandatory with both the labyrinth and mazes, but with the labyrinth, continuity is guaranteed by the form of the design. With mazes, continuity is achieved only through a player's skill.

In other words, there is a single, uninterrupted trail within the walls of the labyrinth. There are no decisions to make as we travel through a labyrinth, since breaks in the walls, detours, and dead ends are foreign to the labyrinth's design. We simply follow a single winding path. The maze form, in contrast, is filled with as many structural challenges as can be devised. A maze may have several points of entry and even more trails spinning off from each of these beginnings. There are no limits to the false paths, detours, and dead ends that can be worked in to a maze. And, as we explore David Russo's mazes, this distinction between the two forms becomes much clearer. David Russo delights in filling his mazes with as many types of challenges as possible.

With this important distinction now made, we return to the shared history of mazes and labyrinths, reverting back to the other school of thought that uses the terms interchangeably, since this represents the more familiar manner in which these terms are used in popular literature.

The labyrinth was born in antiquity. A series of complex rooms and galleries or passageways, some or all of which were submerged underground, the labyrinth was associated with royalty and used for spiritual initiation, to symbolically contain power, and to entomb the royal dead. Although the classical writer Pliny includes a Lemnian and an Italian labyrinth in his list of the four great labyrinths, it is the other two on the list that have captured the imaginations of great thinkers and storytellers from Plato to the South American magical realists. These are the Egyptian labyrinth outside Crocodopolis and the legendary Cretan labyrinth.

The two share many characteristics, including claims on the origin of the name. The Greek historian Herodotus recounts a visit he took to the Egyptian labyrinth, which was built by Pharaoh Amenemhet III, who ruled Egypt from approximately 1842–1797 B.C. Herodotus described a two-story building surrounded by a single wall and measuring slightly less than a third of a mile in length and a fifth of a mile wide. Nearby was a pyramid two hundred and forty-three feet in height, and to the east, Lake Moeris. The building contained one hundred and twenty courts and three thousand chambers laid out in complex and deceptive patterns. Half of these rooms were on an upper floor located above ground, while the other half were on a separate underground floor. Herodotus was permitted to travel the rooms in the upper floor, whose ceilings were stone and whose walls were covered with sculpture. But he was not permitted to visit the labyrinth's sacred lower tier, which contained the tombs of the kings who built the labyrinth and those of the crocodiles sacred to Egyptian religion.

The legendary Cretan labyrinth built by Daedalus for King Minos and which was said to be entirely subterranean has been placed by some scholars at the palace at Knossos on Crete, although no physical trace of this centerpiece of classical mythology has been found there. Like the Egyptian version, the Cretan labyrinth also housed a sacred beast of power: in this case, the half-man, half-bull beast called the Minotaur, who was the source of King Minos's worldly power. The only humans allowed to breach the limits of Minos's labyrinth were the seven young people of each sex offered in sacrifice to the Minotaur yearly to guarantee Minos's continuing rule. Unlike the Egyptian structure, the Cretan labyrinth was made up of a complex pattern of alleyways, not rooms and galleries. It was the hero Theseus who finally liberated Crete from Minos's rule by offering himself as one of the Minotaur's sacrificial victims in order to penetrate its lair, while unrolling behind him a ball of red thread, given to him by Minos's daughter Ariadne, so he could retrace his steps once the beast was slain. Theseus's success led to the destruction both of the labyrinth and Minos's empire, and the ball of red thread has become an enduring symbol for memory. Its wide sphere of influence is visible in some of Russo's more fluid, woven maze paths.

Both Egyptologists and classical scholars have claimed origin of the word labyrinth for their respective fields of study. Scholars of ancient Egypt have said "labyrinth" is ancient Egyptian for "the temple at the entrance to the lake." However, general opinion seems to favor the classical archaeologists. These scholars cite numerous drawings in the palace at Knossos of the double axe called the labrys and associated with the bull as the origin of the word. Labra is the Greek word for alley. In its classical context in association with the sacred bull, the labrys was a symbol of illumination on a par with the cross, so whichever origin is correct, the labyrinth was born with connotations of personal triumph, a keeper of civilization, spiritual initiation, and a source of mortal danger or ultimate sacrifice that, traditionally, must be risked to experience profound growth or transformation.

By the fourth century B.C. the labyrinth had also penetrated the kingdom of the mind. In a dialogue, Plato describes and draws a circular labyrinth resembling the Cretan model. He identifies it as the single, unwavering universal path that all souls must successfully cross to reach the underworld. The labyrinthine center of power is seen from a new perspective. Once the central mystery is touched, it loses its supreme importance. The person who successfully crosses its threshold sees the path from a new vantage. It becomes marginal, transitional, a passageway from this kingdom to the next, which will hold another maze whose center will lead to yet another new dimension. As evocative of the birth experience as it is of initiation and growth, passage is another innate property of the maze David Russo grasps intuitively.

In Asian and tribal cultures, labyrinth patterns also have sacred properties that seem more likely to be part of the fabric of popular culture than the elite halls of kings. In these cultures, the labyrinth is likely to surface in two dimension as a pattern drawn on rock or paper, foreshadowing its later use as a game. Some of the ancient Celtic line designs discovered etched in the rocks of northern Europe and patterns found on cave walls resemble a two-dimensional version of the Cretan labyrinth.

In one common variation, a series of concentric circles is penetrated by a single line that begins beyond the outer circumference and ends in a dot at the maze's very center. To the contemporary eye, this design clearly evokes the fertilization of the egg by the sperm and brings the labyrinth image into the fold of many ancient symbols that represent opposites while also adding a new pair, that of male and female, to those evoked by the royal Mediterranean labyrinths, thus contributing to the maze's talent to express the mysteries of fertility.

Tamil women in southern India still draw labyrinthine patterns on the threshold of their homes for protection during the winter solstice period when the sun is considered to have "died." One of the patterns they are expert in, called Brahma's knot, is an infinity symbol. Here the Western labyrinthine fusion of life and death finds an Eastern counterpart.

The ideas of sacred space and sacred pattern fuse in the labyrinth patterns found in the mosaic floors of medieval Gothic cathedrals. The designs often include the names of the cathedral's builders and, occasionally, bishops. While some sources maintain no reason for the patterns' existence has been convincingly argued, others recount that pilgrims used to follow these mazes on their knees until they reached the centerpoints and that some were actually called "The Jerusalem Mile." The Egyptian sacred city of the dead of antiquity has evolved into the Christian kingdom of heaven.

The three-dimensional labyrinth resurfaced above ground in seventeenth-century Europe, this time as a living game. Life-sized formations of hornbeam, holly, or yew were carefully planted and tended, again for the entertainment of royalty and nobility, who would challenge themselves by entering the living labyrinth, locating its center, and retracing the complex path to the world beyond its boundaries, much as Theseus did in Greek myth.

While in the East maze patterns seem to have always been part of the web of spiritual tradition, in the West the maze appears to have permeated popular sensibility much later and as a game. Following the example of the living mazes in palaces like Hampton Court, new variations sprung to life on village greens throughout Europe, blending the applications of maze as center of the city and center of power (this time, popular instead of elite) with the challenge of the game. Soon the maze also made a transition to paper, again as a game, and often for children.

Artists also began to execute the mazelike work. The letters of some illuminated manuscripts contain labyrinthine patterns, as do the rose windows of Gothic tradition. As times changed, the maze also surfaced in art with a more secular orientation: Leonardo da Vinci's drawing *Concatenation* resembles both mandala and maze. In it, as a single line weaves a complex pattern of delicate knots and arabesques that radiate and revolve outward from a circular center. In *Concatenation* it is easy to see Ariadne's thread looping and flowing through the treacherous alleyways of the labyrinth, and also Brahma's knot.

The twentieth century has made its own contributions to uses for this constant yet constantly changing creation of human consciousness. Scientists have lent their own interpretation to the maze's ancient purpose. They have discovered that the maze is a very good learning tool, particularly when paired with the ubiquitous laboratory rat, as a useful research device for behavioral science and cognition.

And, of course, artists like David Anson Russo are making the maze their own. In his work, David Anson Russo infuses both of the maze's innate gifts with his own unique vocabulary. In each one he is liable to draw on color, symbols from myth and spiritual experience, pattern, dimensionality, and both the confidence and philosophy of the martial arts to sharpen the enjoyment of the game and to deepen the meaning of the accomplishment.

The interweaving of a variety of cross-cultural symbols into the trails of each working maze is Russo's unique elaboration of this ancient form, dating back to at least the late Paleolithic period, circa 15,000 years ago. This theme resonates perhaps even more strongly with the rug weavers of the Orient than it does with the more austere alleys and chambers of the four mazes of antiquity mentioned by Pliny, Herodotus, and Plato. Russo himself would probably point out that some of this is a result of two-dimensional versus three-dimensional perspective: looking down on a paper maze or on a carpet the player can easily recognize the symbols a design contains, while someone who follows a three-dimensional pathway can only see what each trail looks like from within. Each form is reduced to a series of turns and curves, the overview is lost.

But one suspects Russo's choice also betrays a likeness in temperament between this contemporary artist and a gifted Asian weaver. For both, art is a very personal but also very universal expression of spiritual orientation, which is revealed through pattern and symbol. And the execution of the maze and the carpet requires painstaking skill and patience as well as artistic vision.

A single Persian carpet may contain more than half a million knots and take a lifetime to complete. And in their own way, David Russo's mazes exact as much devotion. Each path of each maze is drawn freehand by this artist, who wants to give a subtle, woven, organic feel to every maze he makes, even though some are more liable to appreciate and experience his creations as games. Some of the mazes also require many different layers of color to achieve the desired richness or subtlety. Strategically, the planning of each maze also requires much painstaking attention. Psychology, graphic subtlety, and a design of maze paths so there are many ways to pursue their intricate bends and turns and also achieve the goal—all go into the execution of each of the thirty-nine mazes in this book and all add to the triumph and depth of the experience and maximum entertainment.

The inclusion of many symbols, often in the form of maze paths within the design, also adds to the experience. Some symbols recur from maze to maze, giving a unity to the whole endeavor. Just as, in Eastern thought, the movement of enlightenment is seen to be a spiral, so that at each level of growth we are faced with familiar problems that must be solved in novel ways, so might we find ourselves reconnoitering, in Russo's vortex maze, a spiraling force that draws us inward and which is the maze's solution. And in the Five Swirl maze, we encounter a series of outward-swirling spirals from which we must break free. Similarly, in Russo's Saber-tooth Rider maze the X, a universal symbol of death and transformation, represents the penultimate step before the triumph of the sacred kill. Meanwhile, in a maze called Inception, the same symbol is traced in white and becomes part of the universal birth symbol and the player's starting point.

Throughout the book, we also find a rich collection of infinity symbols woven into the maze paths; some are clover-shaped, some have the geometric precision of their Chinese forebears, still others resemble looping Möbius strips. But however similar each type may look from maze to maze, Russo is careful to vary the exact path one must take to exit this symbol because, as the artist likes to remind us, each variation is "just another way of approaching infinity."

Perhaps the two points of view presented at this essay's beginning regarding the definition of maze and labyrinth can be resolved by considering seminal ideas of two great Western thinkers, one ancient and one modern. In Platonic thought, a single, abstract, idealized form exists for each worldly object, which is then replicated endlessly in earthly reality. This basic concept, one of the building blocks of Western civilization, resonates with a more recent idea of Carl Jung's.

Like Plato, Jung was also stimulated by the labyrinth. And Jung noticed that certain shapes, patterns, images, and characters surface again and again throughout human civilization and imagination, manifested in mediums like religion, art, and dreams. The mandala is one archetype expressed, among other places, in coiled spheres, serpents, clocks, rosetta stones, and of course, in mazes. Jung believed that although each archetype can manifest itself as individually and as often as each person's experience of it, an archetype is also an independent, single stream of energy kept alive in the medium of the collective unconscious of humans.

It's easy to see each of the many intricate winning paths in every one of David Anson Russo's mazes as another variation of that single, clear path to enlightenment, whether that path is idealized clearly in the Platonic mind or flows softly and endlessly through the Jungian collective unconscious. Whatever name we prefer to call it, this enlightening game clearly has an enduring role in human history. Constantly renewing itself from age to age to appeal to successive cultures and generations, it continuously offers us new and varied opportunities for pleasure, knowledge, growth, and play.

—Deborah Bergman

THE ULTIMATE
Maze Book

I

Open Access

THE PURPLE OUTER BAND of this maze represents the seventh, or crown, chakra. According to Eastern spiritual tradition, seven chakras, or wheels of energy, circulate spiritual life force, or prana, throughout the body. Located at the top of the head, the crown chakra is said to be the seat of higher consciousness. This is where you start your journey, all knowing. Later, you will be challenged. The process of solving this maze mirrors the life process of rediscovering knowledge we already know as souls. "Open Access" describes the multiple pathways among which you must choose to achieve the final integration of higher consciousness and life experience symbolized by the central white ring. You must discover how each of the seven rings is connected to the others and to the central ring as well. Beware of the many dead ends and seductive paths that could pull you far from your final goal.

These are what make this maze difficult, and also quite enjoyable.

Begin at the arrow at the upper left rim. End in the swirling eddy at the maze's center.

2

Seven Rivers

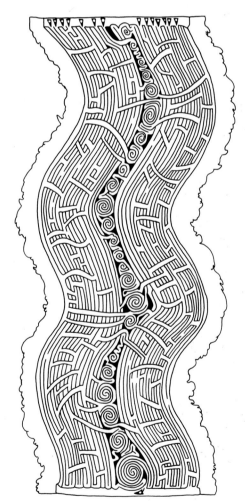

A BASIC SUBSTANCE of medieval alchemy was the *aqua nostra,* the water of life. Only by following its flow did one reach the core or kernel of purified substance, which Carl Jung later interpreted as a potent symbol of the self. In many world traditions, bodies of water also symbolize spiritual experience and the unconscious. The common message these different traditions send might be nothing more complicated than this: follow the path of least resistance through the multiple, moving currents of life experience you encounter, and you will reach your goal more rapidly and joyfully, whatever that goal may be. In this maze, there are seven rivers on each side of the central swirl (in numerology, seven is the number of spiritual experience). Each river holds ten other streams that lead elsewhere in the maze, but only seven of each ten are truly viable. This is a very difficult maze. Be careful not to jump trails. And if you are sucked into a whirlpool, be prepared to go with the flow: the maze may let you go in a place quite different from the one where you started. You'd be wise to follow the lead of the fish swimming down the sides of the maze. They instinctively swim with the current of the tumultuous waves they encounter. Fish also symbolize the living contents of the unconscious, the archetypes it buoys generation after generation, with its nurturing, moving life energies.

Begin at any one of fourteen arrows at the top. End at bottom arrow.

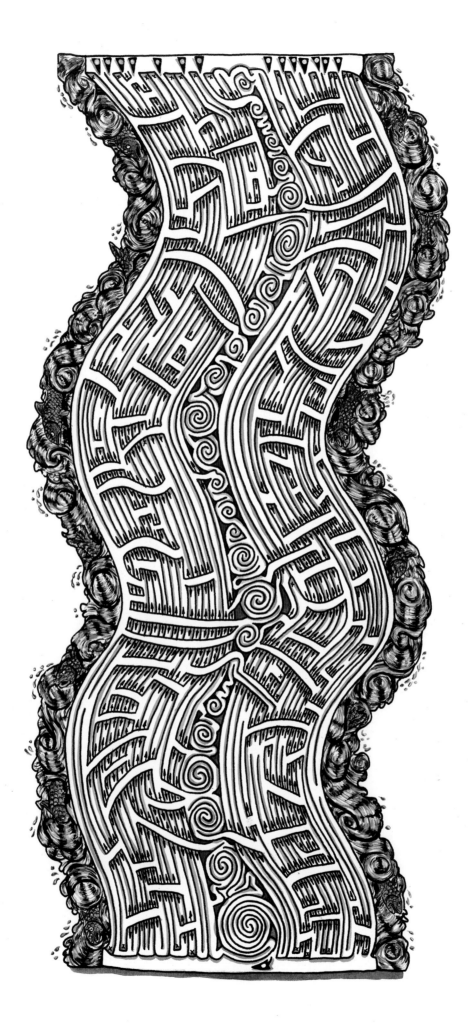

3

Makai

MAKAI MEANS "toward the mountains" in Hawaiian. In many ways, makai is also synonymous with the process of solving a maze. To choose the best trail up a mountain you stand at the bottom and look at the top. However, the trail you decide upon from this vantage point is not always the one that will take you all the way to the summit. Once you begin your climb, you may discover trails that are more direct, scenic, challenging, or reliable than the one you originally chose. You may even find successful paths no one has ever taken before. Maze-solving is a similar

process. It's almost mathematically certain that no one else has ever taken exactly the same path you will to reach your goal: your journey to the mountaintop is unique. The colors and shapes of the Makai maze embody the experience of climbing the mountain. The four black arrows in the center of the white swirl where you begin show you that you can move in any direction to achieve your goal. The richness and harmony of the maze's color hint at the richness of experience that is now yours, because the mountain is a wondrous place to be. The way to reach this maze's goal is through the orange-yellow area in the center. Here, be careful to choose the right road. You are now so very close to your goal that there is only one that will take you there.

Begin at the four arrows in the center of the white circle. End at the black arrow in the arrowhead-shaped white area below. (If you look straight down from the starting point to the finish point, you will see that together they make a spear.)

4

Islander

THE ISLANDER MAZE is inspired by the colors and patterns of the South Pacific. The patterns in the outer layer reflect the twisting, vinelike shapes of the jungle. They surround a more geometric interior. Both of these are aspects of Hawaiian art, which often reflects the natural beauty of the islands. In this maze, the underlying wash of color is as soft, organic, and unpredictable as a journey through the islands can be. In the circle at the top runs the Native Hunter. Like you, he wishes to reach his goal as quickly as possible. Your goal will be to reach the color-oriented, swirling eddy

in the maze's center. As you progress along this maze's paths you may sometimes find that you are in the middle of nowhere and that every road leads to water, just as you would if you coexisted with the ocean waters that shape South Pacific culture. You'll also find pinks and purples that represent the flora of Hawaii, and greens of the rain forest. The swirling eddy that is the centerpiece of the maze also symbolizes the hypnotic power of the water which dominates all the colors and moods of island culture. Pass by the false entrances and merge with its swirling essence.

Begin at the larger black arrow that points toward the Runner in the top ring. End at the central swirling eddy.

5

Pleiades

THE PLEIADES, or Seven Sisters, are the stars that make up Orion's belt in the constellation of the same name. Some esoteric traditions name the Pleiades as the center of the Milky Way Galaxy, and also as the point from which life force emanates. Alcyone, the brightest Sister, is thought to be the exact center, and she is the central of the seven star-arrows that mark the start of this maze. Other esoteric creation myths relate that we humans are of Pleiadean ancestry, stranded by a disabled Pleiadean craft many aeons ago. A highly technological people, to survive, the earth-bound Pleiadeans became a highly intelligent tribal society. According to the myth, they tested the healing qualities of the

roots and plants of our planet and initiated the Chinese medicines and prana-based healing arts like acupuncture that are still so powerful today. This maze is a gift to Pleiadean lore, which, whether myth or reality, has reacquainted many of us with wonder and helped us to enlarge our inner horizons. The universe holds many surprises, and we as a species may have the delight of experiencing them.

Begin at the center arrow at the top. End on the violet Beam Ship (spacecraft).

6

Saber-tooth Rider

THE SABER-TOOTH RIDER MAZE explores the spiritual relationship that exists between hunter and hunted in tribal societies. To this end, it also draws from the sacred designs and inscriptions of the daggers of the East, which announce each weapon's power by depicting the mystical and heroic deeds it has performed. The hilt of this dagger-shaped maze contains the image of a man holding a triangle in each hand. This hunter rides the head of a saber-toothed tiger. He risks his life to tame the untamable beast and share its sacred life power with his people. The heart carved in the saber-

tooth rider's chest is a shamanistic symbol for life and vitality. Powerful wizards in tribes like the Native American Iroquois were said to hide theirs outside of their bodies to thwart enemies. The two X's near the blade end of the dagger are symbols for physical death. And in the tip of the dagger lies a man's head holding its prey's heart in its mouth. This image symbolizes survival and triumph.

Choose any one of the three triangles at the hilt to begin. End at the arrow inside the heart at the tip.

7

Leo's Den

THE LION'S TAIL-SHAPED GLYPH at the top of this maze is the astrological symbol for Leo. This glyph comes to us from ancient Egypt. In astrology, Leo the Lion traditionally embodies the qualities of charisma, leadership, self-expression, and play. The sign is also linked with the Sun, which is associated with the personality or ego. In both myth and history, the charismatic hero or ruler who liberates his people is a traditional Leonine figure. But solar liberation and the joyful freedom that is its result can also come to a community in the form of a shared idea or vision. This communal vision—be it one of a pristine environment, healing, a just and loving society, or simply a mode of personal growth—can liberate each member from individual limitations and in so doing open up new avenues of self-expression, vitality, and personal power for all. The red area in the center of the maze symbolizes the Lion's enormous heart and courage, and the fingerlike starting trails depict the outreaching Leonine personality. The warm aura of solar yellow that surrounds the lion's head and flows down through the center of the maze transmutes these individual qualities into a universally nurturing glow. The swirling circle where the maze ends celebrates the feelings of wholeness, joy, and growth that can result from basking in Leo's light.

Begin at any of the thirteen arrows at the lion's head. End at the arrow in the center of the large, swirling circle below.

8

Twenty-nine Cubes

THE BRIGHT COLORS and architectural structure of this maze evoke the conscious contents of the mind or personality, or one of its most archetypal images, the great city of Babel. Every so often, when we build a great structure in our lives—be it a career, a relationship, or a certain sense or interpretation of self—either life events or inner guidance hint it might not be a bad idea to explore this structure down to its very roots in the subconscious, in order to reacquaint ourselves with the soul essence where it started. As you travel from the top to the bottom of this maze, you might think of your progress as plumbing all the levels and building blocks of the unconscious, breaking down and reexploring the structure of the personality or any sort of creation to find whether it is soul truth. In its impulse to create and become, the soul is capable of infinite beautiful expressions such as this one.

SPECIAL DIRECTIONS FOR A THREE-DIMENSIONAL MAZE *Begin at the white arrow in the top cube. End at the white arrow in the center cube in the bottom level. As you travel through the twenty-nine cubes, you will travel from one end of the maze to the other. There is sometimes only one successful choice for moving from each cube to the next, although there are a few trails that will take you to that choice. You can also travel through the cutouts on the side of each cube to reach the next cube.*

9

Vortex

A VORTEX is a naturally occurring whirlpool, observed with the naked eye in water, air, and chemical reactions. The vortex pattern is very strong. It attracts and devours other configurations of matter and energy. Yet, what lies on the other side is unknown. Thus, the vortex is a potent symbol of destruction of the old and familiar leading to creation of the new and untested. Perhaps the most compelling natural vortex is the black hole. Named in 1968 by theoretical physicist John Wheeler, the black hole is a collapsed star whose surface gravitational field is so strong that all matter, even light, is drawn inward and loses its identity. The vortex phenomenon is also sacred to many earth religions. Wise men and women in many traditions sense sacred power spots on the earth's surface which radiate strong vortex energies. These energies are then harnessed during ceremonial rites that usher in new levels of power

and awareness, and also by individuals, who use them to clarify different aspects of the life path. The Vortex maze symbolizes an inevitable life transition. A moment has arrived when fate appears to have radically altered your life direction. No matter what you do, eventually you will be sucked into the center vortex. It is possible you will have to sacrifice a dearly held aspect of your identity to achieve your heart's desire. All that is certain is that once you approach, you make an irrevocable leap of faith into the new, which is vital to achieving your goal.

Choose any of the six anchors as your beginning point. End in the central vortex.

IO

Five Swirl

THE FIVE SWIRL MAZE was inspired by a series of satellite photos of the ocean which showed how, from a distance, the waters that cover two thirds of our planet often move in enormous swirling eddy motions not apparent at sea level. The swirling eddy, an essential life symbol, is an inverse vortex: instead of pulling matter in, it pushes it out. Several of the configurations looked exactly like the five-swirl configuration in this maze. The clusters of four rotated outward, like these do, into a more complex band of smaller eddies that made up an outer ring. Eventually they merged into more placid, glasslike expanses, represented here by the smooth geometrical patterns along the maze's edges. You'll start this maze at one of the four arrows that point away from the small swirl in the center. This first swirl will lead you outward, into the systematic movement of the others. Once within it, you must pick the right path to escape the pattern's unrelenting pull. Once you cross the outer ring and into calmer waters, take time to admire the blues of the sea and all the gradations of sunlight reflected in its waters. Finally, you'll be drawn up into a final tiny solar swirl and then to your goal, represented here by the illuminating light of the sun and the swirling joy of its solar flares.

Begin at one of the four arrows in the center of the maze. End at the orange swirl underneath the sun at the top.

I I

Ueshiba Do

IN JAPANESE, Do means "The Way." Morihei Ueshiba (U YEH-shiba Doe*)* is the name of the man who created the flowing art of Aikido, which means the Way of Peace and Harmony. ("Ki" means spiritual life energy, similar to the Indian prana.) Aikido was designed through several other martial-arts styles Ueshiba practiced in his lifetime. This is a powerful, strong, and solid maze that is also very internally harmonious. It is a visual image of the inner strength and harmony that is achieved through the practice of Aikido, and it is also a spiritual blueprint for the Self. The purple near the center of the maze depicts the spirituality within us all. The powerful blue in the very center depicts the light within, the order in one's life. The interweaving grid of trails that cover this area is loosely woven, because while a chosen life order may be stable, it need not be permanent. It can be changed at any time. The magenta vibrating in the upper circle shows inner strength. The tiny blue sphere between magenta areas is the ego, in actuality a very definite but very small part of our entire being. The red and orange extensions of the maze flowing out to the sides depict the power and fire that flow to our extremities when our Ki, or life force energy, wells up unobstructed from the very center of our being. The upper green circle, where the maze begins, contains a Chinese symbol for long life. This maze is dedicated to Ueshiba.

Begin at the arrow pointing into the green circle at the top. End at the upward-pointing arrow near the bottom.

12

Tri-pod

THE TREE is sacred to almost everyone. To shamans, the ceremonial journey through the levels of the world tree from root to canopy is also a journey through the many layers of the universe from earth to heavens. For Jewish Kabbalists, the mystical Tree of Life with its ten fruitlike spheres, each an essential quality of being, is the source of all that is. The Tree is also a symbol for the Trinity: the Father is the root, the Son is the branch, and the fruit symbolizes the Spirit. In this maze, the number three is also important, as the three seed pods are the individual sources for three separate maze trees that blend into one large tree shape. As you pursue the hollows and swirls that emanate from the center seed (your starting point) you will also follow the life path of the tree. This path progresses from seed to stem through the beautiful canopy of leaves and on to the bearing of fruit. It is in the luscious red fruit of these trees, fashioned here from infinity symbols, that the promise of the seed comes to its fullest fruition in all the knowledge, passion, and richness of life. And you, like Eve, must take the risk of sampling this fruit to successfully complete the Tri-pod maze. Within one fruit lies the gateway to the finish, which will bring you full circle to another seed and a fresh source of all the potential of life.

Begin at the trail that begins with the central seed pod near the bottom of the maze. The end lies in one of the other two seeds.

13

Praying Mantis

I N C H I N A , men and women look to the praying mantis to teach them about softness and power. Some aspects of the way this beautiful, graceful, and deadly fighter moves seem strikingly familiar to humans. Its triangular head turns slowly from side to side. In its habits and demeanor the insect is very particular and deliberate. And, the praying mantis grasps things in a prehensile manner, with its "hands." Its power, softness, and beauty inspired tai ch'i praying-mantis style, the martial art that bears the creature's name. This delicate maze celebrates the praying mantis's particular beauty and strength, and scrutinizes the praying mantis from below. The crisscrossing and curling paths that move up the center of the design represent the vulnerable ridge of belly and breast the creature usually protects while fighting. The cool colors echo the softness of its movements, and the purples in particular indicate the spiritual riches that can be found in contemplating the praying mantis. But the creature's coolness is part of a more complex identity: be sure to notice the twin triangles at the start and the golden stylized figure-eight infinity symbol below and how the maze begins and ends with sparks of warm, energetic, courageous red.

Begin at either one of the two colored triangles at the top. End at the golden infinity symbol at the bottom.

14

Seven Chakra Lotus

IN THIS MAZE you will travel the spiritual anatomy of the human body. Seven chakras (Sanskrit for "wheel") move spiritual life force from the base of the spine to the crown. The basal chakra, symbolized by a red square, is the center of strength, survival instincts, and sexual energy. The spleen center, source of courage and self-esteem, is traditionally a soft orange. Here, it holds the balanced forces of yin and yang. The sacral chakra is the source of personal power, thought, and the fire in vision. It is represented by the powerful triangle with its strong, stable base and tip pointed toward the sky. The pink and green heart chakra is the source of love, growth, compassion, and balance. The intertwined triangles of its six-pointed star symbolize the integration of all opposites. The throat center, focus of creative expression, is traditionally sky blue. The pyramid is the traditional symbol for the brow or third-eye center,

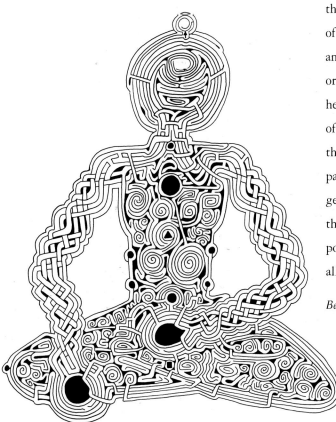

the source of intuition and inner vision. And the lotus blossom of the violet crown center symbolizes the flowering of the soul and the transcendent unity of that experience. Minor chakras, or nadis, also focus energy through the body; some are shown here in blue at the knees and along the torso. The meridians of energy that run within the physical anatomy and that are the basis of Eastern healing arts are evoked in the white maze paths. The layers of color that surround the seated figure suggest the rich multiple layers of the human energy aura. And the hands are posed in "dhvanasana," which is said to be the position of the humming, resonant force that knits together all the still and moving things of the universe.

Begin in the yin-yang symbol in the abdomen; end in the lotus at the crown.

Full Circle

THE MANDALA is the archetypal symbol of whole experience, a state in which all aspects of the self have been fully integrated and realized and "psychic center of the personality" reigns, as Carl Jung has said. In Sanskrit, mandala means "magic circle." Practitioners of Eastern religions meditate upon the mandalas, which create specific states of awareness that foster spiritual growth. Mandala images, often circles with an outer rim and a central reference point, also flourish worldwide in dreams, mythology, and the arts. Primitive, Mayan-oriented patterns are the idiom for this mandala-inspired maze. Aside from the central yin and yang, there are no particulars; each twist and turn is merely part of the emblem for the full circle movement. The deep, rich teal where you start places you in the oceanic depths of the soul. As your path radiates outward, so will the color rings, from light to dark. But notice that when

you reach that outermost, vibrant pink ring you will find you still have a close connection to the colors at deepest center. At the finish you will find the same depth of color that marked your beginning. But this time the rich color has transmuted to the rich purple of the crown chakra. The Full Circle maze may be used as a more active version of the ancient Eastern teaching tool, the mandala. Trace its complex paths to experience how the start and the finish are one and the same. For the whole soul, all knowledge is always present and needs only to be accessed.

Begin in the teal hemisphere in the left side of the central circle. End in the violet hemisphere in the right side of the central circle.

16

Split Cube

HERE THE STANDARD MAZE on paper gets a radically different treatment. To solve this maze you will have to work on a three-dimensional plane of thinking. Each of the four levels must be conquered to accomplish your task. Do this by dropping from plane to plane. This maze is a "breakthrough" maze. The process of solving it mirrors those moments when, after toiling and laboring to solve a problem, you suddenly "drop through" to a new reality and new problems to conquer. Your new perspective not only allows you to solve your problem but also makes it become insignificant by opening whole new horizons of life experience. The Split Cube maze may look simple. In fact, it is relatively difficult. But once you finish it you will have learned how to master space in a totally new way.

SPECIAL DIRECTIONS FOR A THREE-DIMENSIONAL DROP-THROUGH MAZE *In this maze, your goal is to drop level by level. A hole indicates the place you move from one to the next, and an arrow shows you where you land. If you land on a black dot with nowhere to go, you may find yourself backtracking up a level to find a better opening. Begin on the top box at the arrow. End on the bottom box by going through any hole that indicates an exit.*

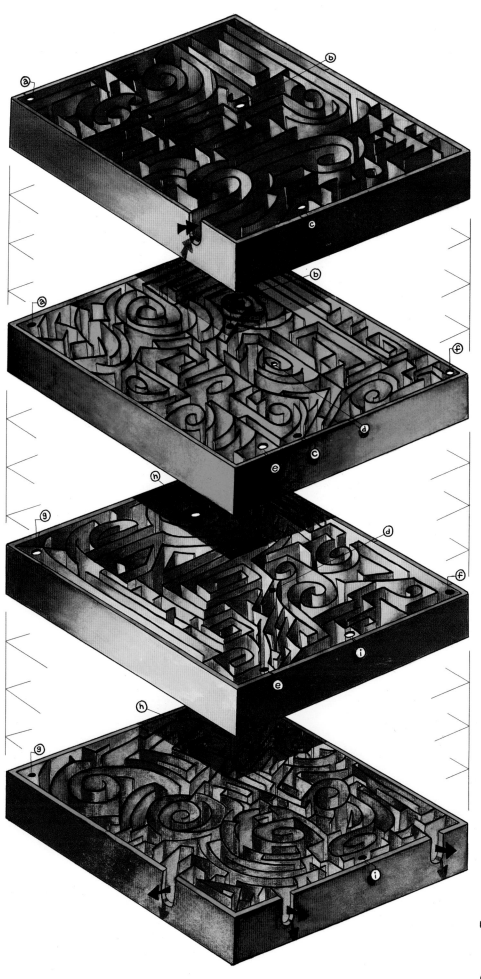

17

Swirling Eddy

IN THIS MAZE, movement flows from the center toward the periphery. Solving it is like traveling outward on ripples of water. This maze is quite difficult. Like the Tarot image of the moon, and inspired by the movements of water, its flow echoes that of the dream, subconscious, and intuitive states, indeed, any life experience that reminds us that the singular quality of truth is in fact made up of many levels and aspects of perception. Life often flows more effortlessly when we accept that multiplicity is actually an aspect of clarity and whole meaning. If you look at the top left of the outer ring underneath the finish arrow, you'll see that this outermost rim of color itself is a swirling eddy, and that in it the hues of the spectrum swirl out beyond the maze's boundaries. Further layers of color swirl out from the center in waterlike movements beneath the trails. The central swirling eddy where the path begins soon becomes a

braid. It circles and braids once more before coiling out into different aspects and patterns, and finally into multiple rings of trails thin as cloud as you reach the outer ring. When you reach the periphery, take care not to jump trails as you travel the seven-path ring, as this is part of the maze's deception. The experience of sailing free of that last trail and into white infinity is singular and definite. But that perfect triumph is only made possible by the multiple aspects, trails, and illusions embraced within the eddy, which are, after all, just aspects of the perfect unity of the circle.

Begin in the very center of the maze, in the swirling eddy. End by following the arrow at top left out of the maze.

18

Inception

THE STAR at the top of this maze is a symbol for birth. This very profound symbol is actually composed of a plus sign, which symbolizes life, and an X, which in many cultures stands for death. Here the plus sign is drawn in rainbow colors, while the X is drawn in white, the color of purity. Deep in the background, the birth symbol radiates the colors of spirit and imagination, violet and indigo blue. In quality, the Inception maze is very masculine or "yang." But if you look down the center of the maze, starting with the twisting spinal shape in the top center, you will see it draws its form

from the body of a woman. You might use these feminine paths as a point of orientation as you pass through the initial layer of entwined figure-eight infinity symbols, which represent the multiplicity the infinity experience contains in space and time. Next, encounter a layer of eighteen ankhs, combining the Egyptian symbol for life and the ancient Hebrew number of life. As you travel further down the maze you will meet a pair of blue-purple turtles, an ancient Eastern and Native American symbol for life on earth, and then a row of square Chinese infinity symbols. The Inception maze's varied symbolism mirrors the physical wisdom of the body, which holds within it such a rich variety of organs, whose processes intertwine to give it life. The maze's center, a looping flower filled with deep red, symbolizes the female creative principle. Below, a navel ring lined with yellow is surrounded by paths that create the female reproductive system. When you reach the yin-yang embryos that are this maze's finish, you will know a little more about how the fleeting, twinkling split second of inception gains the wisdom of matter and reaches life form.

Begin at the birth symbol at the top of the maze. End at the yin-yang embryos near the bottom.

19

Four to One

MANDALA FIGURES often include four elements, evoking all the separate components that knit together into one whole. And true to this maze's theme, there is one path that begins at the four arrows at the top of this maze that will take you all the way to the single finishing point at bottom. And the three circles within the maze's diamond-shape outline make another four to one. The floral trail pattern inside the top circle is found in New Guinea, Hawaii, and Japan. Here, it stands for the different paths and different positions or perspectives one can take in life, yet share a common route with others. The rest of the maze emanates from this pattern. The smaller central circle is a swirling eddy, and the lower circle is also floral in nature. The rich yellow, gold, and orange background evokes fire, an ancient Western image of creativity and purification. In the East, fire is associated with cosmic bliss. As Philip Rawson remarks in *The Art of Tantra,* "the incentive [for spiritual devotion] . . . is an occasional vision, as if one were to glimpse the fire of a raging furnace through a crack in its wall, of the cosmic bliss which is an all-embracing love. . . ."

Begin at any one of the arrows in the undulating figure at the very top of the maze. End at the single arrow at the bottom of the maze.

20

Journey into Yin

THIS MAZE celebrates the yin, or feminine element of life force, which each of us possesses and can access. Many words have been used to describe the power of the yin, but some of the most common are receptive, quiet, intuitive, and soft. This very powerful maze's force is quite feminine and flowerlike; the paths and colors delineate the delicacy, softness, and gentleness of the yin. The violet coloration honors the deeply spiritual essence of these qualities. Look closely at the paths traced above the violet in top center to find a woman sitting in the lotus position, a soft peach aura radiating

around her shoulders. This is one of the more challenging and intricate mazes to complete. Yet the goal you attain here is well-earned but by no means final. As you touch it you also touch the Chinese symbol for long life and the center of a six-petaled flower. Much new experience, knowledge, and growth will blossom open for you once you have journeyed deeply and gently into your own yin.

Begin at the double arrow at the top of the maze. End at the small yellow circle in bottom center, the Chinese symbol for long life.

21

Chi Circle

IN JAPANESE, Chi means four. This is the maze of four circles. The circle symbolizes the boundaries of the self or a community of like selves. The circle's diameter is always somewhat larger than the physical body, so while the circle protects, it also expands. The members of earth religions and other groups often gather ceremonially in circles for unity, strength, and spiritual connection. Some forms of meditation invite the practitioner to surround himself or herself in a circle of light. Martial arts also teach that within the circle that surrounds you, you are the center of your own universe. That universe moves when you do, and that movement is the subject of the Chi Circle maze. The Chi Circle depicts four of the infinite number of moving center points of the soul in motion. All meld together, showing you the center points of who you've been and where you're going. The maze trails also emulate the circle shape. In

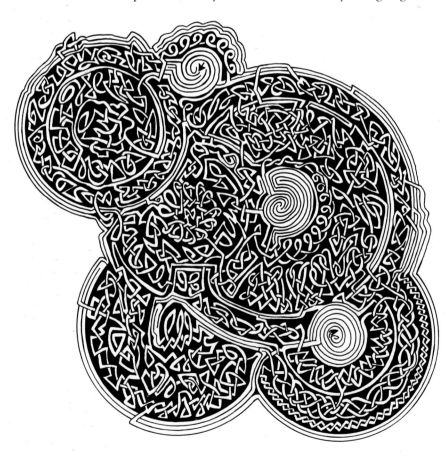

the largest circle, a swirling eddy of color whirls outward below the trails. And be sure to notice the spirit and strength of the circle in the upper left, which radiates the higher consciousness of purple, burns with orange and yellow vitality, and begins with black blood-red life energy deep inside.

Begin at the arrow in the white swirl near the top. End at the arrow in the white swirl near the bottom.

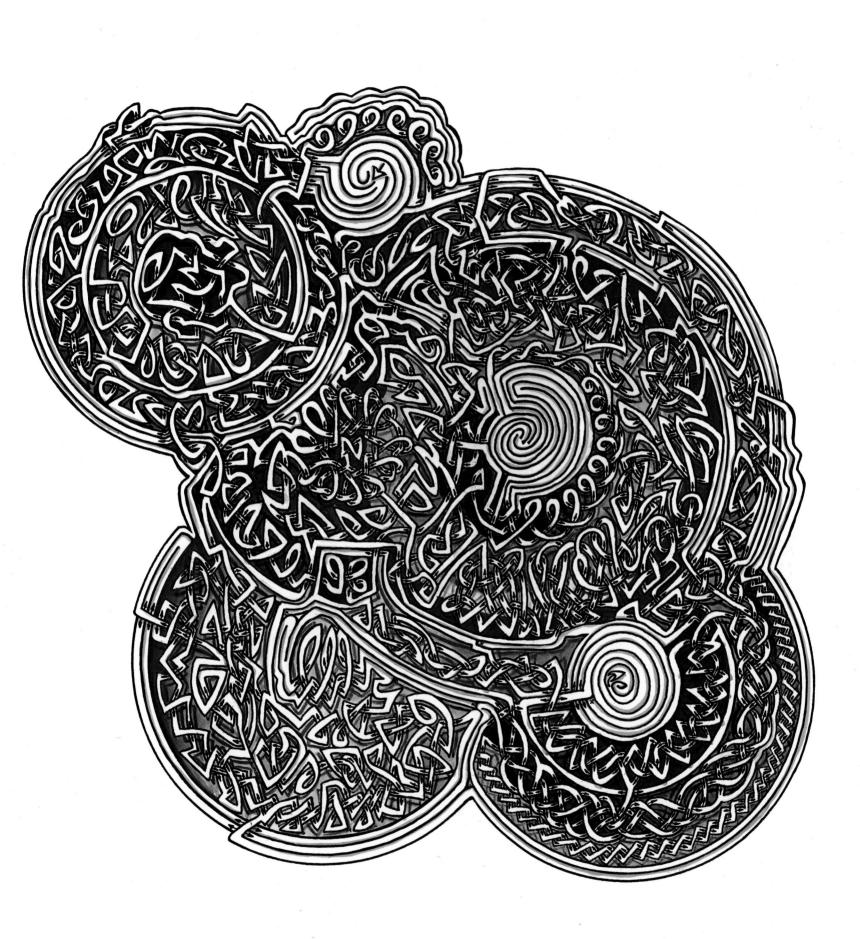

22

Ronin

IN JAPANESE the Ronin *(RO-nin)* is a "wave-tossed man." In feudal Japan the word was used to describe independent Samurai warriors (most of their counterparts were protected by and accountable to feudal lords). Independence had its price: the Way of the Ronin was also known as the Way of the Hard Life and the Rocky Path. The Ronin maze reenacts this path. When you start this maze, your goal will be right before you. But to attain it you must travel the farthest reaches of the maze. Here you will encounter more than the usual quota of twists, turns, and dead ends. You will also experience the geographical richness of the Ronin's path; the mountains, forests, seas, and villages that unfold along the edge of the entire maze. Some of this landscape is gentle, but often it is quite rough. The Ronin often walks along the edge of the cliff and must do so carefully, for fear of falling. But he also has a rich and eminently portable source of support—a lifetime of Samurai teachings. And if you persevere until you reach the main artery of the maze, which travels down its center, it will lead you straight into the maze's heart. Here, finally, you will be able to choose among several entrances to the finish. The Rocky Path is always the more difficult one, but its rewards are so much the richer.

Begin at either of the two arrows above the Samurai sword. End in the curling wave at the bottom of the maze.

23

Interior Box

THE INTERIOR BOX is a kind of three-dimensional room or pit. You must travel it as though you were on the inside—a mouse actually crawling through these walls. Like the life-sized garden mazes and labyrinths found throughout the world, this maze requires you continually to change your perspective to win. Although the trails are fairly simple, the changes in perspective make the challenge quite difficult. Observe all trails closely, because they can be deceiving: many open paths will actually look closed unless you regard them from a three-dimensional perspective. And remember, if one wall is not completely flush against the next, you can pass through. This maze is an exercise in creating your own reality, because the paths are designed in such a way that if you think you can solve the maze easily, you will. So if you have a question about whether or not you are going to be successful, give yourself the benefit of the doubt. And if you really want to challenge yourself, try doing this maze in the mirror.

SPECIAL DIRECTIONS FOR A THREE-DIMENSIONAL MAZE *Begin at any of the seven white triangles that point into the maze area from the outer edge. End at the single white triangle in the maze's very center.*

24

Celtic Clover

THE WOVEN CLOVER SHAPE at the maze's center is adapted from a traditional Celtic rendition of the classic symbol of luck, and of a plant known for its gentle but powerful healing properties. The woven patterns in the green bands near bottom left and right of the circle and in the bottom half of the red outer circle shapes are also Celtic in origin. The patterns in the top half of the red circle are adapted from macrame. The thread is a universal symbol for divine energy. In fashioning the knots that helped make his fishing nets and shelter, primitive man was also metaphorically tying the universal thread of life into specific forms that would sustain him during his lifetime. Ancient Celtic crosses were often rendered in woven patterns, and the knot is also one of the classic cross-cultural symbolic representations of infinity. The man and woman illustrated at top represent the yin and yang aspects of the

maze. The green-clad, leprechaunlike gentleman carries the Celtic shillelagh or walking stick, which represents magic or wisdom, while his rosy-cheeked companion carries flowers representing femininity and fertility. The verdant colors of this maze evoke the lushness of Ireland. This maze will challenge you as it leads you in and out of its complex interweaving patterns, but it is also highly entertaining, as any visit with the Celts would surely be.

Begin at the black arrow at the top that leads into the maze. End at the black arrow that leads out of the maze.

25

Triplex

THIS MAZE explores the dynamics of and wisdom offered by the number three. It is shaped from three circles, and ends in the classic Eastern symbol for three at the bottom. Both start and finish are surrounded by coiled trails braided from three different strands. There are many different ways to approach a path or solve a problem. One advantage of the threefold approach is that it is a much more stable one than the ever-fluctuating yin yang. Unlike this classic symbol of duality, the triangle has a broad base that amply supports the narrow tip that reaches toward the sky. The addition of a

third element can make situations and experiences seem more tangible, permanent, result-oriented: in numerology, three is the number of creativity. Some say the birth of a child solidifies a family. And in the martial arts, bars or locks always consist of three points—a base made of two contact points and a third point of pressure. In the Triplex maze you will be led through three different particular paths. You can see them as life paths, or as the strands of energy in a situation that you are dealing with. The wisdom of three teaches that in every situation there is always a positive, negative, and middle ground. And in this maze you will find there is a path that will lead you directly to the finish, a path that will not, and a third path that will guide you to another point in the maze, from which you may reach the finish if you choose your subsequent path wisely.

Begin in the center of the small swirling eddy at the maze's top. End at the eastern trinity symbol at the bottom.

26

Multi-Nebulae

IN THE UPPER-LEFT-HAND CORNER of the maze lie the swirling forms of the classical Eastern trinity symbol, which you will approach as you enter the Multi-Nebulae beneath the white arrow. Below it, Celtic-inspired weave patterns link spheres of blue and green surrounded by a violet weave. At bottom right, notice the white, dense paths of a square and two swirling eddies. Above, organic, wavelike paths to the left break and resolve into a kaleidoscopic, prismatic sphere of color that emanates outward from a central star. A tiny white spark radiates from that star's center. This spark is where you will complete the maze. The multi-nebulae is multi-dimensional. It depicts those life journeys in which many

diverse and very beautiful patterns and experiences are encountered, but appear unrelated. Even when the path of this life becomes difficult, as it does when the maze journey becomes hard and boxlike in the lower right, each experience is connected to every other experience. So as you solve this maze, remember that although the task of navigating any one figure may appear to become all-absorbing or overwhelming, you (and your efforts) are still part of a single, clear, and dynamic whole. Consider the design of churches and temples: there are many stained-glass scenes in a single cathedral and many beautiful patterns of sacred energy on one mosque wall. Together, these unique patterns coalesce into one beautiful shelter.

Begin at the white arrow. End in the white spark at the center of the multi-colored star.

27

Scarabaes

THE SCARABAES, or Scarab, is a seminal symbol of Ancient Egyptian religion. First found in the Late Old Kingdom (c. 2686–c. 2160 B.C.), it is often discovered scattered through burial sites, and on seals, amulets, and other artifacts of Egyptian religion. Its inspiration is the scarabaes, or dung beetle, which lays its egg in a ball of excrement and then consumes it, eventually reaching the chrysalis and the new life within. Egyptian religion revered this process as a microcosm of the regenerative cycles of nature and the daily rebirth of the sun. Most importantly, it symbolizes the enduring

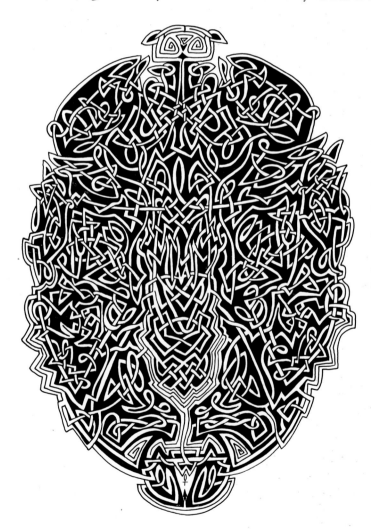

human soul. If you look in the center of the Scarabaes maze you will see the glowing life force stretching from the head of the beetle to the tip of its tail. In this maze, you will find yourself patiently exploring the entire surface of this luminous power. When you reach the tail you will be rewarded with the Ankh, the Egyptian life symbol and a precursor of the Christian cross. You have probed the darkness and tapped the golden glow of the soul. Your odyssey of regeneration is complete.

Begin at the arrow at the top of the maze. End at the arrow in the tail that points to the Ankh, the symbol of life.

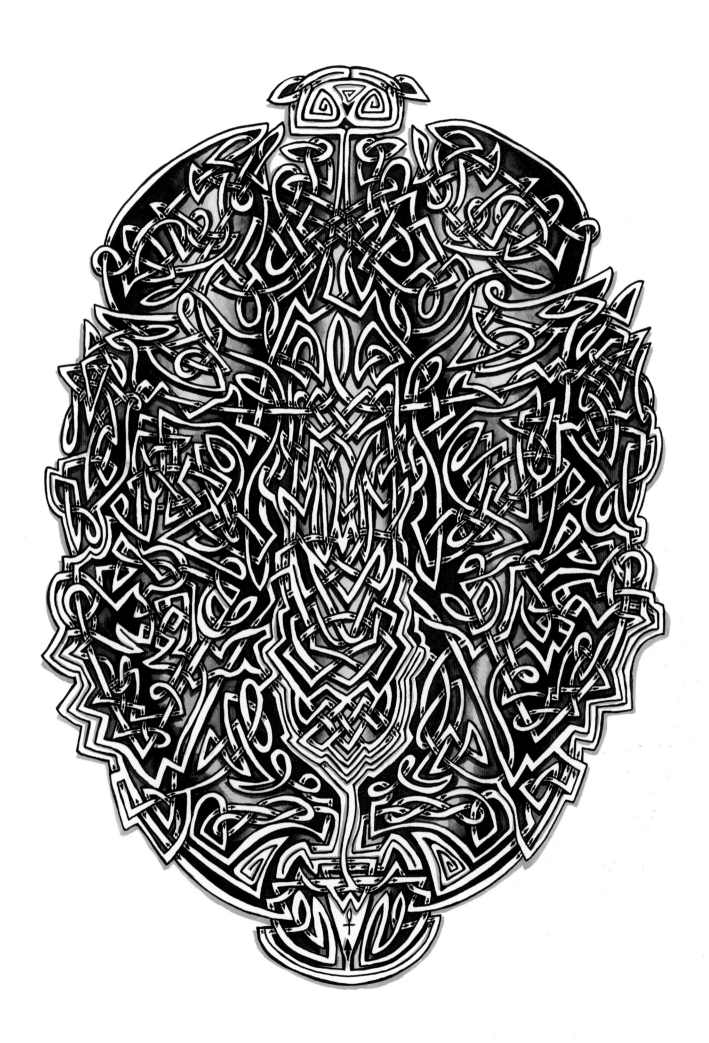

28

Spouting Bunny

NO PATH or achievement obtained, however profound, is truly complete without the experience of humor and lightness. This is the role of the Spouting Bunny maze. Some of the most serious cultures have the most humorous artwork, and this maze was inspired by a tiny Indian sculpture of a stubborn elephant being pushed and cajoled by scores of men pulling it from the front and pushing it from behind. This maze is intended to evoke some of that sculpture's movement, lightheartedness, and fun. The trails of this maze are also very pretty, particularly around the bunny, where they loop

and swirl with playful abandon. The bunny image comes from an actual bunny fountain on the island of Kauai. Be sure to notice the light, fluffy, billowy clouds in the sky. The flower symbol within the green box at the right is a symbol for four, as is the fuchsia flower at bottom left. The maze's colors are also fun and lively, and be sure to notice its golden outline, which for all its joy and levity also strongly radiates spirituality.

Begin at the yellow diamond above the bunny. End in the center of the swirling eddy at bottom right. (The two arrows in the center of the fuchsia area at bottom left indicate that this is a through area.)

29

Gauntlet

A MEDIEVAL TERM for an armored knight's glove, the word gauntlet also describes an important V-shaped military formation from the same period. The wide ends of the V disguised the trap. An army lured into a gauntlet did not see its enemy until it had reached the center of the V formation. By then, the soldiers would be surrounded by their foe, who closed ranks behind them. The Gauntlet maze also pulls you in toward the center. Your challenge lies not in being able to head in the direction you want to go but in escaping the elaborate design you encounter when you get there. There are

surprises and false paths. And the intricate infinity symbol in the maze's center will require painstaking attention. The gauntlet symbolizes a leg of the life journey that seems easy at first. Yet the more you progress along it, the narrower and more filled with obstacles it becomes. On such a path, if you lose heart and turn back your difficulties will only increase. You can only overcome by finishing what is started. Then truly you will have achieved.

Begin at the curved arrow at the top. End at the black dot in the smaller infinity symbol at the bottom.

30

Combustion

T HE COMBUSTION MAZE invites you to experience what it is to be fire. Its colors are fire colors: notice the inner golden light, the red and orange glow, the licks of green and blue near the maze's dancing edge. And it is shaped like the flame whose shape constantly tosses and turns and flickers above a candlewick. There are an unlimited number of forms a flame can take as it burns. It takes each for just a fraction of a second, never to appear the same way again. The interweaving center of the maze represents the movements of the heart of the flame that sits atop the white wick. This area is where the fire's power resides. And the asymmetrical trails that loop, knot, and flicker above explore the

million and one movements of the fire that looks exactly the same yet entirely different each time we gaze upon it, just like a person that we love. Also notice the small white pinnacle at the top. This is where the maze starts and it also represents the flame tip, the place where the flame will usually come to a head at some point. In astrology, fire is also connected with self-expression and creativity. So, we may look at the constantly changing but eternally present flame as a model for the light of vision, power of expression, and receptivity to the new that are all so essential to both artistic creation and personal growth.

Begin at the arrow inside the white tip of the flame. End in the center of the white wick below.

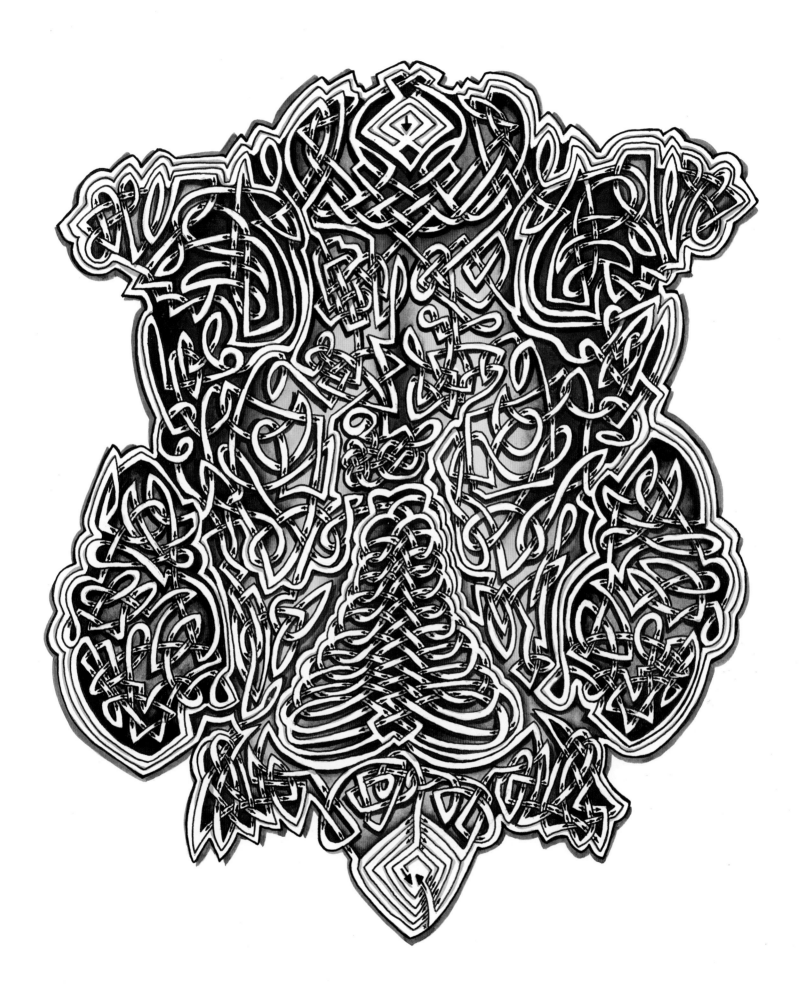

31

Infinity Nine Blossom

THE DRAGON, also known as the mythical coiled serpent Ouroboros, is one of our most ancient symbols of rebirth. A mandalic creature, he reconciles all forces in his intense power. In his front talons, he holds the earth and clouds, symbolizing matter and spirit. His back talons hold a skull and an Egyptian ankh: the dragon is master of both life and death. At the end of the dragon's coiled tail lies the heart of humanity, and his white beard demonstrates that even though he is an immortal creature, he is intimate with the processes of time. Eagle wings show his close ties to that other creature of rebirth, the phoenix, and allow him to transcend both matter and his own baser serpent nature. His third eye shows his capacity for spiritual sight. Around the dragon unfold the eighteen petals of the Infinity Nine Blossom. If you look closely you will see that each of the petals is a unique hexagonal maze. The ancients knew that hexagons are one of only three types of regular polygons that, like the cells of a honeycomb, leave no gaps between them when placed one next to the other. They therefore considered the hexagon a powerful conveyor of the deep order and harmony of the universe. In this maze, you must pass through each of these hexagons to approach the center of the Infinity Nine Blossom, which is your goal. As you do so, consider seeing them as individual incarnations or lessons to learn as you approach the central serpentine mystery of life and death. Remember, it is the dragon's power we tap to regenerate from one stage of growth to the next, to keep growth an eternally dynamic process.

SPECIAL DIRECTIONS FOR A THREE-DIMENSIONAL DROP-THROUGH MAZE *In this maze your goal is to "drop-through" level by level. To move from hexagon to hexagon, jump from any hole to any corresponding black dot. The numbers are there only to show you which hole goes with which black dot. Some holes will take you to true paths; others are dead ends. Begin at the orange arrow to the right of the blue hexad at the top. End by reaching the dragon via one of the four arrows at the center.*

32

Inner Sanctum

BE READY to execute a tightly coiled eddy as soon as you penetrate the outer limits of the Inner Sanctum. If you succeed, your path will broaden. Choose your way carefully when you enter the ring of thirteen circles. Thirteen is a special number. As Joseph Campbell says in *The Power of Myth,* this number universally represents that crucial single step into the unknown past the order represented by the number twelve. In this maze, the thirteen circles represent the sun and the twelve astrological signs, which are also doors the soul can choose among to come to earth. In this maze, some roads will take you closer to your heart's desire, others will make you wonder whether you really have the means. Successfully navigate the woven paths that connect them and you will be reunited with your own deepest center, the ruby-studded ring. The gem is a potent image for purity, transformation, and the self.

Begin this maze at any one of the four arrows at the outer corners. End at the ring of ruby-red diamonds in the middle.

33

Cohes' Tsugiashi

ONE DAY I HAD AN IMPULSE to take my many martial-arts belts and braid them together. When I looked at all the different colors I realized that all my different levels of skill in the martial arts were very interwoven as well, just different aspects of a single set of teachings that I approached from different perspectives along the way. As my martial-arts teacher likes to remind me (and this maze is dedicated to him): it is not the goal that is desirable, but the journey to the goal. This journey is also known as Cohes' Tsugiashi (COE-hees Tsoo-gee-ASH-ee), or the process of "one foot following the other." This maze began with that process and the braid of belts, which you can find

reinterpreted in the interwoven, crisscrossing design traced over blue and purple in the center. In these central trails all is as intertwined as progress in martial arts, where the first and last skills mastered are intimately related. From the red power base to the higher consciousness of violet, the colors of the maze indicate the different aspects of spirituality. The taut interweaving trails in the red circle that surrounds the finish appear to pull outward, like a trampoline. To traverse this area successfully, imagine you are walking gently on rice paper. Martial-arts teachers advise we do this throughout life in order to best hear what is truly going on about us.

Begin at the bottom of the maze at the purple eye and three red arrows. End in the round, red "trampoline" cluster at the top.

34

Seed

THE POTENCY of seeds lends itself to powerful spiritual symbolism. In South America, seeds found caught in a drought or buried in sand for long periods have come to full flower when watered. This deep life source held within, this special gift that can flower at any time, makes the seed a powerful metaphor for the human soul. As the saying goes, "In the acorn lives the mighty oak." Spiritually, this age-old wisdom seems to say that everything that exists begins in a dream. As the source of the roots that hold the plant firmly in the ground, the soul seed is also what gives each of us roots or

stability as we reach for the heavens. In this maze, four shoots spring up quickly from the seed, lifting its power upward as its latent energy becomes active and transforms the dream into the strong, tenacious substance of a mighty jungle tree. The double and triple maze paths and thick layers of outer bark show how the basic vinelike strength multiplies during the growth process and the dream power of the seed gains the tenacity of life experience. In this maze, you become the sun and follow the inner paths of this tree's strength from top to seed, nourishing the trunk as you work all the way through it and back to its source. Like each soul, this seed is unique, flecked with beautiful points of violet.

Begin at the arrow at the top of the trunk. End at the violet-flecked seed on the golden background.

35

South Pacific

IN HAWAII, there is a saying: respect the ocean, or it will bring you to your demise. This saying inspired this maze, which explores the Polynesian Way. Rich with South Pacific color and pattern, its focal points are three key moments in the life-and-death cycle of the food chain. In the top circle, where the maze begins, a small fish is swimming. In the central circle, a large fish bears down on the smaller one. In the final circle where the maze ends, the smaller fish has been consumed. Small wave designs surround the first and last circles, showing the repetitive, wavelike movement of this cycle and symbolizing the cycle of new life that begins with death. And the reds and oranges emanating from the maze's center also represent the life-and-death process. The bamboo that edges the shield is key to shelter and tools in Polynesian society. It makes the maze resemble a warrior's shield. The beautiful flowers that grow from the edges depict some of the beauty that is nurtured by this rich, organic life cycle. The maze's long, sinuous central trails emulate the vinelike patterns of the rain forest. We humans are part of this powerful cycle of life and death, too. As we swim out into the ocean, we enter the richly interwoven marine food chain unprotected. And as we approach large waves in the surf, we risk their terrible power as well as their ability to carry us high and fast above the water to the shore.

Begin at the circle containing the yellow fish. End at the circle containing the purple fish consuming the yellow fish.

36

King's Crown

THE VIBRANT hues and intricate trail shapes of the King's Crown maze are inspired by the colors and shapes of European stained glass. At the apex of the maze, the paths trace the shape of a ruby- and emerald-studded crown. The black arrow that points to the starting point is the crown's peak. The intricacy and opulence of this maze evoke the quality of royal existence. The life of royalty is customarily a very full one, rich with a very special and unique intensity of history, education, ceremony, and tradition. Elsewhere, the appearance of a golden crown in a dream can foretell honor, and a king usually augurs good fortune. And, of course, in many religions the crown of the head is considered to be the area where higher consciousness blends with ordinary consciousness. Thus, on another level, the King's Crown Maze celebrates the inner wealth, intricacy, and fullness available to be tapped by all of us and shared as a king would, with the rest of the world.

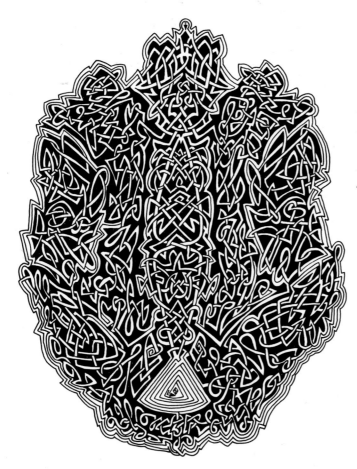

Begin at the black arrow at the top of the maze. End at the ruby at the center of the series of white triangular trails near the base.

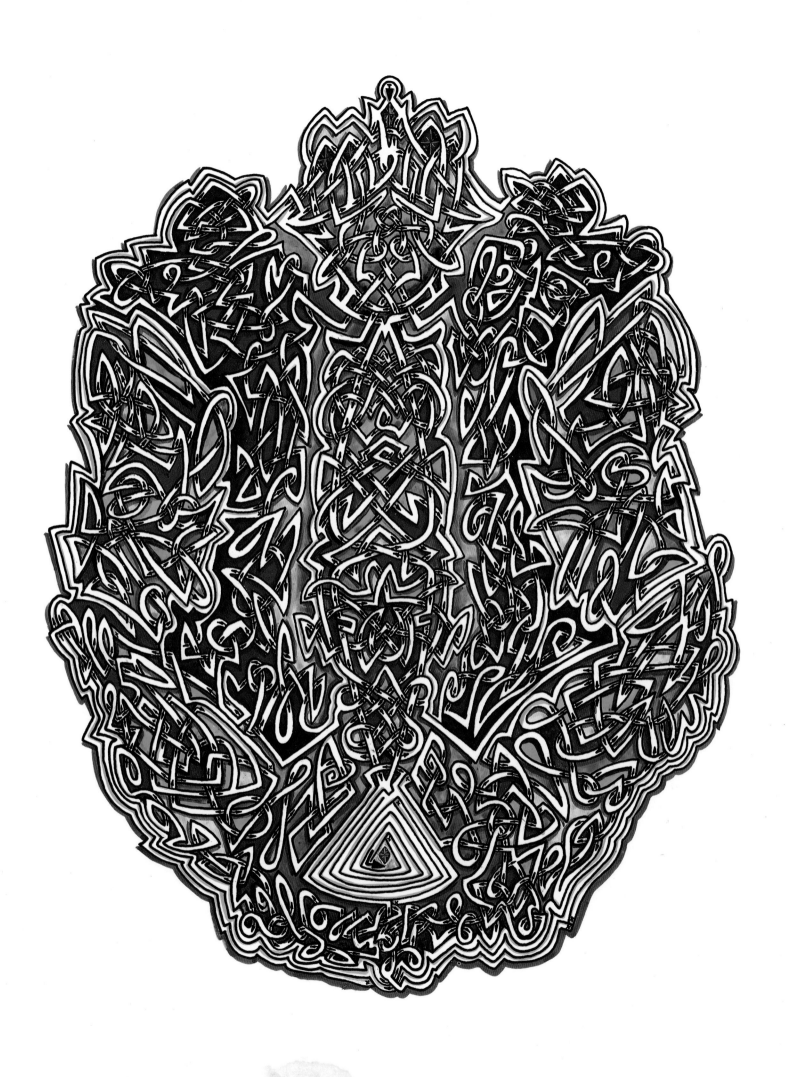

37

The Eye of the Hurricane

THE EYE OF THE HURRICANE is part of the swirling eddy maze series. This eddy is made of air and electrical energy as well as water. The maze actually contains a double hurricane—two circles of movement, power, flow, and force that interpenetrate and merge. If you look carefully, you will see that inside each one there is an octopus extending its curving arms in a swirling eddy motion. The eye of an actual hurricane is a calm place to be. But there is no calm at all in this maze. Every path, swirl, and dead end is tumultuous and kinetic and holds the power to propel you straight to the finish as well as forever toss you back and forth through its air pockets, winds, and rain. Note the

vibrant, red-magenta background and the outer ring of kinetic waves created by its centrifugal force. Solving this maze is like coming up against a certain kind of obstacle or problem. Once you encounter it, you're instantly absorbed by its power and size. You have no choice but to go with that flow and allow it to take you where it will. The only way to get out again is to let yourself be propelled out the very same way you were drawn in when the right moment comes. The maze will eventually push you out toward the outward-moving ripples, and finally through its edge.

Begin at the yellow arrow in the center. End at one of the two arrows on the right edge of the maze.

38

United Fifty-five

ACH OF THE FIFTY-FIVE CIRCLES in this maze is a tiny maze in its own right. The individual mazes link into a larger one just as tiny cells link up to make the entire human body. And each small maze also represents a living being—soul, person, or entity—that is a unique and precious individual yet also a unique and indispensable element of our vast universe. Solve the united mazes and you will have experienced something new about the larger puzzle of being. Here are some of the maze's secrets: the repeating pattern is almost cellular in nature; each cell is based on an ancient infinity symbol; there is a reason for the color of each of the cell mazes. You must deduce the rest, and what each of us deduces may be as unique as the essential something each soul contributes to the unique quality of the whole. In this maze, the goal is to reach the central Nirvanic white light that the larger weave of being supports. The white light is surrounded by a golden flower, Chinese mandalic symbol and magical blossom of the alchemists. But remember, there would be no center if there were no outer unity to hold it. The white light stands for nothing and everything, it is at once the most and least important thing about the fifty-five united mazes.

Begin anywhere on the outer rim. End at one of the four arrows at center (part of your challenge is to find out which one).

39

Yin Yang

AT LAST the yin yang gets a final turn on its own. Colors and three-dimensional shaping make this maze, which is less difficult than some, more dynamic than most. As in all three-dimensional mazes, be careful to watch where you are going and to avoid jumping trails. Yin and yang are actually the two principles contained in the Tao, which means the way or path in Chinese, and in the context of Taoist religion has come to mean, loosely, "the way the universe works." And the way it works is through yin and yang: energies that are cool, dark, moist, and receptive and energies that are warm, light, dry, and active. Symbolically, each occupies half of the circle that represents the Tao. In the classical diagram the line that separates them is equal to one half the circumference of the circle, and the outline of each shape, yin and yang, is equal to the full circumference of the circle. As Joseph Campbell notes, "what this diagram represents geometrically is the mystery of one circumference that becomes two and yields, then, the ten thousand things of creation." In relationship with anyone or anything, one partner will represent yin and the other yang. Yet, together, they will represent something far larger than two individuals: the totality that is yin and yang, the way of the universe, the All.

SPECIAL DIRECTIONS *For this three-dimensional maze, begin at the red dot, end at the green dot.*

Acknowledgments

———

TO THOSE without whose help I could not exist as I do. Beverly, Stephen, Ed, Hilary, Paula, Diane, Lorraine, Nick, Hellen, Ralph, Margaret, Sam, Chris and Marion, Seth, Burrie, John, Andy, Peter, David and Jamie, Stan and Donna, the two Alexandras, the Halperins, Genevieve, Karen, Greg, Andrea, Gary, Caroline, Dan, Grace, John, Allan, Sylvia, Patty, Laurie, Deborah, Alan, Carolynn, Lauryn, Paul and Dick, Tsugiashi Do Jujitsu Club, Wailuku Aikido Club, and all my sensei. Special thanks to Richie Havens, Peter Yarrow, Tony Schwartz, and Milton Glaser.

I would like to express my deepest respect and admiration for Edmund Carpenter, the foremost authority on mazes and labyrinths. His words and work will fuel and inspire my work to come.

To all who I have loved, and to all who I will. And most of all thanks to the divine energy who has created that which is my existence.